THE MOON
of the OWLS

The Thirteen Moons

THE MOON
of the OWLS

By **JEAN CRAIGHEAD GEORGE**

illustrated by JEAN ZALLINGER

THOMAS Y. CROWELL   NEW YORK

By the Author

The full moon of January rose into the stars. Its dim light shone upon the rolling mountains of the Catskills in New York. It made the bare trees silver. It made the white snow blue. It turned the needles on a pine tree into glass-green spears. And it then gently woke the great horned owl who slept beneath their pointed shadows.

The owl stared into the glowing forest. To him there was no night. He had eyes that took the white light from the moon and stars—reflections from the land and clouds—and made the darkness into day. He saw a snowflake on his great hooked beak. He saw a twig fall on the mountainside. The night was bright as noon.

The great horned owl was two feet tall. His wings could reach four feet across. His feet were bigger than a boy's hand, his talons long as darning needles. His feathers were colored gold and brown and gray and black and white. His yellow eyes were ringed with frames of black. His throat was white.

The owl blinked slowly. He listened. No birds sang, no insects strummed. The frogs and toads were silent. It was January, the month of wind and snow.

He turned his head. He did not see the woodchuck or the bear. They slept in dens as did the skunk and chipmunk. The bats were gone. Some hung in hollow trees and under jags of cliffs. Their hearts beat slowly. They breathed but twice in fifteen minutes. Their temperatures were low. It was the hibernating season.

And yet, the forest was not still. The owl could see a movement here, a scurry there. The moon had risen and the foxes and deer were walking. The rabbits leaped. The mice came out. The minks and weasels flipped and ran. A mole made snow heaves in the meadow.

The owl lifted up his pointed ear tufts. He then ran his beak along a wing feather. It snapped against his body without sound. It was fringed with tufts of down. These made the owl as silent as the moonlight

2

when he moved, as quiet as a falling star when he struck his prey.

The owl swung his head and glanced across his land. He saw the mountain that he owned. He saw his meadows and his high dark cliffs. He could not see his stream and frozen waterfall. He could not see his marsh or farm. But every night he checked his winter range. He flew to stubs and limbs and looked around to see if all was well upon his land.

One night he found another great horned owl hunting there. He drove him far away, for to the owl his land was food and shelter for his mate and young. No other great horned owl could share it. It was his home, his kingdom, and his life.

Suddenly he felt alarm. He bobbed and circled on his limb. He did not know why this mid-January night seemed different from the one before. He knew only that every corner of his land must now be checked, each secret niche and valley studied well. He spread his wings and flew.

He soared down the mountain through the trees, seeing every limb and twig but never touching one. He stopped beside the small "bird tree," where many of the daytime birds slept out the fearful night. The tree was old, a beech with pale tan leaves that clung

3

all winter. Among their shelter many of the winter birds slept, their body heat reflecting from leafy roof and walls.

At first the big owl did not see the birds, for they were motionless. Then a cardinal shifted feet. He put the warm one down and pulled the cold one up onto his heated breast. The owl did not strike. He was not hungry. Another feeling stirred him.

His feathers rose and fluttered. He was excited. It was not because the blue jay stared at him from underneath a leaf. It was not because the nuthatch in the

tree hole had awakened and was leaning out to sense the hour and the cold. It was not because the sparrows and the juncos were striking at their bodies with closed wings to keep their bodies warm. These were movements wonderful to hungry owls, but not this night.

The owl flew on without a sound.

His big feet grasped his favorite maple limb. It jutted out above his stream. He swung his head and glanced around. He saw nothing. But he did hear foot-stirs. His eyes followed the sound to the empty crow's nest in the Scotch pine tree. The crows who chased and screamed at him in spring and summer were not there. Last autumn they had flown away. Now they sat two hundred miles to the south sleeping in their winter roost of locust trees. Yet the owl had seen their stick nest move! He focused his eyes. A white-footed deer mouse was standing on his pale hind feet. He was eating bark.

The owl saw the ground without moving his head. With an area of keen sight at the bottom of his eyes, he saw below while he also saw ahead. His sight encompassed sky and land.

A twig stirred above, and bubbles danced below. He turned full sight on the bubbles in the ice-filled stream. A mink swam underneath the ice. Air droplets flowed from his nose to his whiskers to his back, until his brown fur twinkled silver. The mink plunged over a sunken log. The owl watched.

Presently the mink came up. He slipped through a hole in the ice and bounced ashore with a sunfish in his mouth. He put it down. He shook. His water-repellent guard hairs dried and glistened in the moon-light. He gleamed like the surface of a pool, for his fur is prime during the January moon.

The owl did not strike the mink. He knew the animal was as powerful as himself, this beast that threw a skunklike musk when angered or attacked. Slowly the owl turned his head upside down and watched the mink. He saw him eat his fish and dive for another. The owl turned away.

Now the mink passed the nymph of a dragonfly in the stream. It had a long body, big eyes, and six jointed legs. In its jaws was a snail. The dragonfly nymph was turning the snail into a fluid with a potent chemical in its mouth. When it was changed he would drink it.

The dragonfly was eating in the January cold while other insects lay dormant or waited out the winter as eggs. He still moved because the water was warmer than the land or air. Other water insects swam about —not as vigorously as in summer but, unlike the land insects, they were active.

The bees in the trees and the cocoons of moths in the soil were still.

One water creature was the larva of the caddis fly. The mink saw the wormlike animal move in the chimney he had built of tiny sand grains. A trap door opened. The larva leaned out and felt around. Not much food floated in the chilly water. But there were some one-celled animals. He netted them with his feathery mouth parts. Then he pulled himself inside, closed his door, and sorted out the food from the silt. He opened his door and threw out the refuse, closed it once again, and ate.

A water spider was in the stream. She was in a small air-filled diving bell made of her silk. It was inside an empty snail shell. Here in her bubble in the warm water she could live through the snow and the frost that killed land spiders. She was quiet, barely breathing. The mink swam past her. He was going home to his den at the edge of the waterway. He pulled ashore and dived into the snow. He burst to the surface. He rolled. Then he felt tired. He slipped beneath a rock and entered a tunnel. It led down to a dry bedroom among the roots of trees and bushes.

He passed many sleeping creatures. Earthworms that had no eyes to close lay still in their tunnels below the frost line. A beetle grub slept in an earthen chamber. A chipmunk was tucked in a bed of leaves on the other side of a boulder. He was not hibernating as deeply as the bat. He could and did wake up to reach into his mattress for a seed or nut. He had put them there in autumn for his sleepy period when the cold came to the forest. The mink ignored them all. He rolled into a ball and fell asleep.

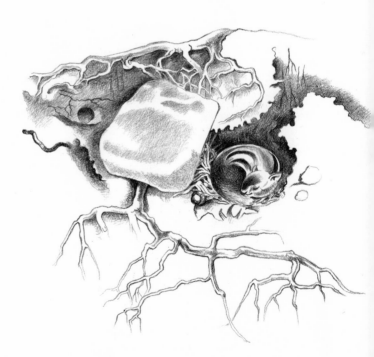

The owl was no longer watching the stream. He was restless. Something within him said "fly!"

He flew up the stream. He passed the empty vireo nest. He soared over the dead limb where the flycatcher sat in summer. The owl had often seen the gray bird fly out and back, catching insects in his beak. Now the limb was empty. The flycatcher was in South America. But under the bark of his limb the eggs of a bark beetle rested. Beside them lay the eggs of a cucujud beetle. Their mother had put them close to the bark beetle eggs so that when they hatched they could eat their favorite food—the bark beetle. The bark beetles that escaped would hatch and eat the bark. The bark would fall off and the flycatcher would eat them both. The dead limb above the stream was a world within the owl's world.

The owl was on his wings. He looked down upon the forest. Icicles hung from trees and the wind made sculpture of the snow. It was two o'clock—a cold hour of the January moon.

The owl arrived at his marsh. He alighted on a willow limb. He folded his wings. He lifted them as if he knew they were dramatic. Then his white throat patch thumped. Something was changing him. He did

17

not sense clearly what it was. His beaver dam? He stared at the logs that held back the stream and spread it out to make the marsh. They were glassed with ice. They did not inspire him, but the beaver caught his interest. He was up and about. The owl watched him swim under the ice. He swam with his webbed feet and steered with his tail. The owl swayed his head the better to see, for the beaver was up to something. He was bracing himself with his tail and feet and pulling with his teeth. Finally he freed an aspen log. He had cut it last summer and poked it into the mud for the fast time of the January moon. The beaver took one end in his mouth and dragged it under the ice back to his lodge. He tugged it into his hallway. In the lodge was a dry room with reed floors and walls of mud and sticks. His mate and young son awoke and pulled in the tasty log. They gnawed, turning the log like an ear of corn. They ate only the bark.

When the owl could no longer see the active beaver he glanced at the marsh edge. A reed stirred. It cracked and fell. Up beside it came a muskrat. His eyes were gold in the moonlight. The muskrat ate the reed. He chewed from side to side. Then he eased into an ice hole and swam home to his dome of grasses and reeds piled high near the shore. The owl watched him. He grew bored. At all hours and seasons he saw muskrats and more muskrats. They were active in the winter, summer, autumn, and spring, by day and by night.

Now the owl felt hungry. He sailed to his oak tree above the marsh. Here he could see far and low. He waited for his favorite food. In an hour it appeared. A white-footed deer mouse burst out of the snow. He ran. Another mouse chased him, angry because the first mouse had trespassed on his land. The owl saw them. He dropped on one. He did not miss. He flapped his wings vigorously to arise, then flew back to the tree and swallowed the mouse. He closed his eyes as he ate him whole.

When he opened his eyes he felt drowsy. But his body said he must go on. He sailed over the marsh edge where the green frogs and bullfrogs were hiding from the cold deep in the mud. He swung over the rocky hillside where the black snakes slept in the cracks

20

of stone. He did not see them wound around each other like threads in a ball of yarn.

The owl coasted over a skunk den. The door was sealed with leaves and covered with snow. No one stirred there, so the owl did not know that the mother skunk and her four black-and-white youngsters of last year were sleeping under the ground.

But the owl did see the trail of a porcupine. It was only a scoop in the snow for it had not been used since December. The porcupine avoided the cold. He was inside a log. Knowing that to sleep was dangerous in the forest, he aimed his quills toward his entrance. The foxes and hounds who hunted him would get quills in their noses if they disturbed him.

Near the porcupine's log rested a cluster of snow fleas. Their eyes glittered, but they did not move. It was too cold. They were waiting for the sun. Even in January it made them dance. Warmed by its heat reflecting off the snow they thumped their long slender legs and sailed three feet into the air. They fell back on the flakes and sailed again. When the sun went down, their legs grew too cold to thump. They waited by the porcupine's log for the sun to come back.

The owl flew over the skunk and snow fleas. Suddenly he beat his wings faster. Far ahead of him a bird winged along the mountain top. It disappeared.

He did not follow the bird. But an old memory drove him down the mountain. He dropped onto a nest of sticks that he and his mate had made. It was high in the crotch of a big sugar maple. He picked up a stick in his beak. His feathers quivered as he vaguely remembered the two white eggs that had lain here last February. He could almost feel them against his breast. He had often protected them from the snow while his mate went out hunting. He could almost hear the cries of the crows harassing him from the limbs above. He could almost remember the crying mouths of the owlets. He could almost recall the pheasants and rabbits he had fed them to stuff them to silence.

The owl felt peaceful. This is what he had been seeking since the moon came up. He stared at his toes. His throat thumped. The nest inspired him. He leaped to his wings. There was something else he must do.

Softly he flew to the edge of his meadow. He took his perch on the elm limb. He shook. Fine bits of fuzz broke off his feathers. They floated on the cold air. When the dull winter feather tips fell, the owl was brighter in color.

Below, in an old woodpecker hole, a starling scratched in his sleep. A feather fell out. A brighter one started to grow in its place.

January begins the brightening of birds. The snow falls, the rivers freeze, but the sun shines longer every day. It is the longer days that start new feathers, and break winter tips off others.

The owl paid no attention to his feathers. He tensed

24

and stared at the meadow. Something was cavorting in the snow. It was the weasel. She was in her winter coat—all white, except her nose and black tail tip. She dove and leaped. She rolled over on her back, flipped to her feet, and tunneled around a goldenrod weed. She was not hunting at all. She was playing with the snow in the moonlight.

The moon was moving downward. A twig snapped. The owl turned. A red fox slipped softly into the meadow. His fur was loose and clean from the snow. He lifted his paw and bit the ice that had frozen between his toes. Then he pounced. Seven quail scattered into the air. They had been sleeping under the snow in a circle, heads out to watch for danger. They shot over the snow in the moonlight like a sparkler. The owl saw one plunge under a bush.

The fox did not catch himself a quail. He had missed. Now he walked quietly across the snow making tracks, one behind the other in a single line.

Not far from him a small mouse woke. The mouse stirred in his nest of plant down and grass strips. He had slept so long he was famished. He stepped into a tunnel at his doorway under the snow and ran down it to a broom sedge plant. He climbed up the grass high above the top of the snow. The weight of his body bent the grass. He rode to the ground searching it for seeds. Only two were left. The quail had been there first. He dove back in his tunnel and scurried to a fork at the rock. He went to the left, hurrying downhill in his subway. In his haste he bumped into a grass blade. It quivered above the snow.

The quiver alerted the fox. He plunged. The mouse felt him and fled. He ran into another mouse's nest. The owner twitched his tail. He lifted his fur. He attacked. The first mouse dived into the snow behind a hickory nut. He breathed hard.

While the mouse shivered beside the nut, the fox caught the other mouse.

The owl watched. He saw something suddenly move under a juniper tree. He focused. The movement ceased. But the owl did not look away—something was there. He swung his head back and forth.

A rabbit flattened his ears, then held them still. The rabbit had seen the fox. Now he saw the head-swinging owl. He watched the owl and the fox at the same time, for his eyes were high on his head and he could see up, in front, and to the side, all at once. He needed to. Everyone hunted the rabbit.

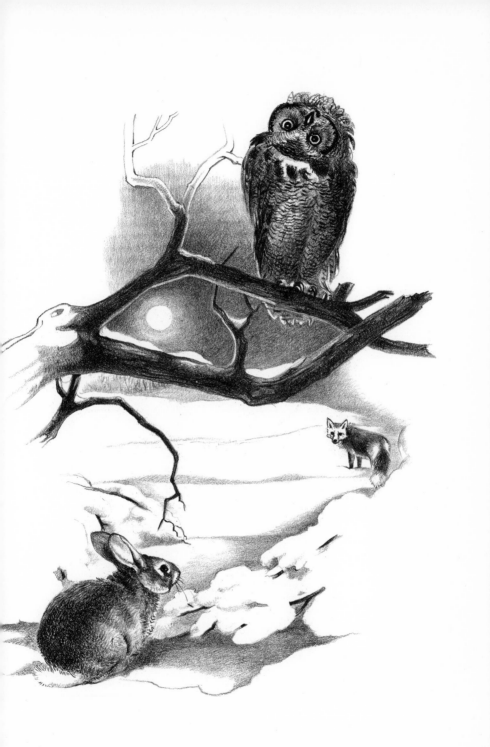

Minutes passed. The fox ate his mouse. The mouse behind the nut went on being hungry. The owl turned his head.

The rabbit, however, still did not move. He could sit all night if he must. He was safe in his winter home —a cup in the flaky snow. It was not warm and deep like a burrow, but open so that he could see in all directions.

The rabbit was alone. Other members of his family were in the meadow but all were separated. Each was under his own bush or tree. They were difficult to find when they scattered.

The owl had forgotten the rabbit. The snow was buckling beyond the juniper tree. He studied it by turning his head upside down to see what was happening.

It was the mole. The mole was digging tunnels in the frozen earth of the meadow. He had too much dirt to handle and had plowed to the surface to push it out. The snow cracked and moved as he worked. When he was finished he poked his head out and sniffed the airy meadow. It smelled owly and foxy. He went down in his subway. His legs were short, but they paddled him along swiftly. He ran all the way to the edge of the underground meadow. On his

31

way he smelled milkweed roots and juniper seedlings. He hustled on, using his nose and body as eyes. His body was like a radio receiver. It picked up messages of vibration. His mind translated them into crawling beetles, digging crayfish, wiggling worms. He received a message from a cocoon that had moved. He dug it out of the earth, and ate it. Then he went to sleep right where he was. He slept as hard as he had run.

The fox jogged off into the woods. The meadow grew quiet. The owl drooped his wings. His white throat thumped. He circled on his limb. Once more he felt the excitement of this night.

He flew on.

He flew over the oldest trees in the forest. They were straight and tall hemlocks. Suddenly he saw something move among the trunks. The owl alighted on a limb to see if this were the excitement he sought. He looked into the large eyes of the white-tailed deer. Her sides were round, for she was pregnant. She had mated in October in the manner of the deer. In six and a half months from that time her fawn would be born. The baby would arrive when the spring wildflowers and fresh grass were abundant.

The doe had been in the old forest since sunset. All day she had been with her herd in the valley where

they stayed for the winter. Just before the moon came up she had felt a stir within her. Her fawn had kicked and turned. She walked away from her friends. She climbed the hill slowly, looking under every oak tree and beech. At last she had come to the sheltering hemlocks. She butted the branches that touched the ground. She trampled the snow and lay down. She peered through the limbs. She felt visible, so she got up slowly and moved into the young hemlocks. They were thicker and denser. She pawed the snow again and lay down. Now she was satisfied. She could not see beyond lacy limbs. Then nothing, she sensed, could see her. She nosed the snow and put her graceful head on her shoulder. Finally she got up and walked softly away. She had found a place to give birth to her fawn. She looked back. She would lie there often before he was born.

The owl preened his feathers. He strutted along the limb. The doe was moving again. He looked down. She was gnawing the lichens on the side of the poplar tree. She pulled down the twigs of a beech tree and ate them. Like the mice and the rabbits, the deer had no green food in January.

Suddenly the owl jumped up. He came down softly. He pivoted and bowed. At last he knew his excitement. It was January and time to find his mate. He needed to hear her again, and to touch her beak with his. He needed to fly and hunt with her. He needed to dance for her on the limbs of the forest trees.

The owl's throat throbbed. He lifted his head. "WHO WHOWHO, who who." His voice tolled like a bell through the moonlit woods.

"Who, whowho, who who." His mate answered him from the cliff on the mountainside.

The owl bowed his head. He lifted his feathers. He spread his wings, then he flew over the tree tops, over the frozen waterfalls and sleeping animals. He drifted to the cliff. He dropped beside his mate.

The January moon slipped down behind the trees. The coldest hour of the year approached. Lakes cracked and boomed as they froze. Trees snapped.

The sun came up. It shone across the snowy stream, the icy marsh, the leafless trees. The owl land looked no different from the day before. And yet, one call across the night had changed it all. The great horned owl had entered spring.

ABOUT THE AUTHOR

The enthusiastic reception that young people accord each new book by Jean George is warmly seconded by their parents, teachers, and librarians. Mrs. George is co-author of DIPPER OF COPPER CREEK, which received the Aurianne Award for the most outstanding animal story published in 1957. MY SIDE OF THE MOUNTAIN, THE SUMMER OF THE FALCON, GULL NUMBER 737, and SPRING COMES TO THE OCEAN all have affirmed her remarkable sensitivity both to the world of nature and to young people.

Mrs. George is a regular contributor of nature stories to *Reader's Digest*. She has held the position of art editor for *Pageant* magazine and has served as a newspaper reporter for the *Washington Post* and International News Service.

ABOUT THE ILLUSTRATOR

Jean Zallinger's illustrations have appeared in many books for young readers. A native of Boston, Massachusetts, she attended the Massachusetts College of Art and received her B.F.A. degree from the Yale School of Art and Architecture.

Mrs. Zallinger lives with her family in Hamden, Connecticut. She is Chairman of Projects for the Women's Auxiliary at nearby Yale–New Haven Hospital, and also takes an active interest in the Peabody Museum of Natural History at Yale and in the Yale Art Associates.